OUR SUPER AMERICAN ADVENTURE

by Sarah Graley

ISBN: 9780993384356

OUR SUPER AMERICAN ADVENTURE

COPYRIGHT 2017 SARAH GRALEY

PUBLISHED BY SHINY SWORD PRESS,
BIRMINGHAM, UK

THIS PUBLICATION MAY NOT BE REPRODUCED OR TRANSMITTED IN ANY FORM OR BY ANY MEANS (PHYSICALLY OR DIGITALLY) WITHOUT THE EXPRESS WRITTEN CONSENT OF THE AUTHOR, EXCLUDING SMALL EXCERPTS FOR REVIEW.

OUR SUPER AMERICAN ADVENTURE

by Sarah Graley

Lettering and Design by Stef Purenins

INTRODUCTION

OUR SUPER AMERICAN ADVENTURE is the diary travelogue of mine and Stef's trip to America in July 2016.

We adventured around Los Angeles, San Diego, and New York, all in the space of two weeks!

We were lucky enough to be travelling over because of comic-related reasons, and those same comic-related reasons are also why it's taken a whole year to find the time to finish this collection of comics documenting what we did while we were there!

So, here's our trip to America, in all its goofy glory!

Enjoy!

- Sarah

ALSO BY SARAH GRALEY

OUR SUPER ADVENTURE

A collection of 200 diary comics about being soppy, eating too much pizza, and living with four cats and one cat-like boy.

OUR SUPER ADVENTURE has been a webcomic since 2012 at oursuperadventure.com and this book was funded through a really incredible Kickstarter campaign!

Available from sarahgraley.com

PIZZA WITCH

Join Roxy, a pizza witch, and George, her black cat familiar, on a quest to get a date with a lactose-intolerant babe!

Can they tackle monsters, magic, and cheese-free pizza ingredients in 30 minutes or less?

Available from sarahgraley.com

RICK AND MORTY: LIL' POOPY SUPERSTAR

Mr Poopybutthole is in trouble, and he turns to the one person he can trust: Summer Smith! She's more than willing to help, but is he telling her the whole truth?

Trade Paperback now available through Oni Press/Titan Books!

KIM REAPER

Becka has a huge crush on fellow student Kim. However, Becka doesn't know that Kim's a Part Time Grim Reaper, tasked with guiding souls into the afterlife!

Issue 1-4 now available through Oni Press!